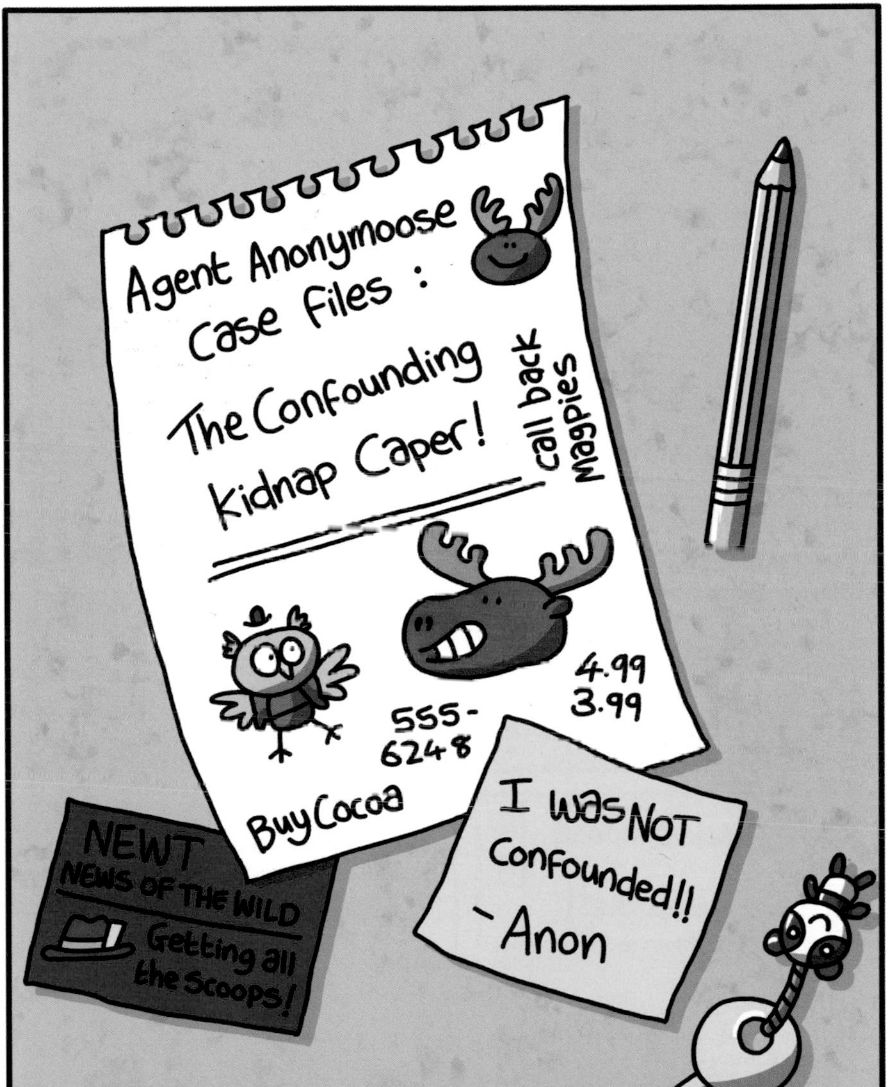

OPERATION OWL

AGENT MOOSE
OPERATION OWL

Mo O'Hara

WITH ART BY

Jess Bradley

■SCHOLASTIC

To my son, Dan, who always inspires me
—M. O.

For Mum, Dad, and Ben x
—J. B.

Published in the UK by Scholastic, 2023
1 London Bridge, London, SE1 9BA
Scholastic Ireland, 89E Lagan Road,
Dublin Industrial Estate, Glasnevin, Dublin, D11 HP5F

SCHOLASTIC and associated logos are trademarks and/or
registered trademarks of Scholastic Inc.

First published in the US by Macmillan Publishing Group, 2021

Text © Mo O'Hara, 2023
Illustrations © Jess Bradley, 2023
This edition published by arrangement with Feiwel and Friends, an imprint of Macmillan Publishing
Group LLC. All rights reserved.

The right of Mo O'Hara and Jess Bradley to be identified
as the author and illustrator of this work has been asserted by them under the Copyright, Designs
and Patents Act 1988.

ISBN 978 0702 32280 8

A CIP catalogue record for this book is available from the British Library.

Printed by C&C, China
Paper made from wood grown in sustainable forests and other controlled sources.

1 3 5 7 9 10 8 6 4 2

This is a work of fiction. Names, characters, places incidents and dialogues are products of the
author's imagination or are used fictitiously. Any resemblance to actual people, living or dead, events
or locales is entirely coincidental.

www.scholastic.co.uk

Book design by Liz Dresner
Color by John-Paul Bove
Lettering by Micah Meyer

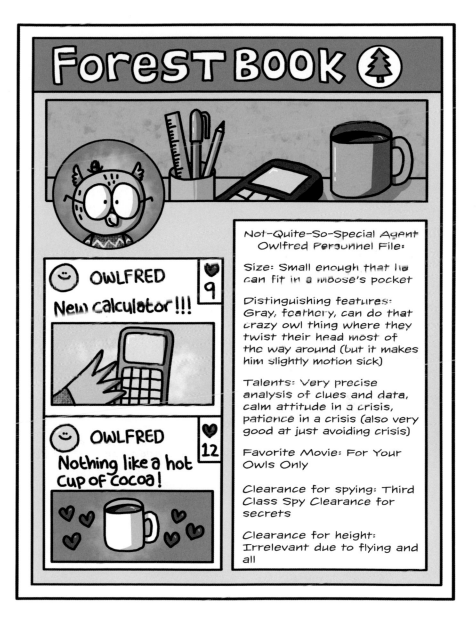

FOREST BOOK 🌲

☺ **OWLFRED** ♥ 9

New calculator!!!

☺ **OWLFRED** ♥ 12

Nothing like a hot cup of cocoa!

Not-Quite-So-Special Agent Owlfred Personnel File:

Size: Small enough that he can fit in a moose's pocket

Distinguishing features: Gray, feathery, can do that crazy owl thing where they twist their head most of the way around (but it makes him slightly motion sick)

Talents: Very precise analysis of clues and data, calm attitude in a crisis, patience in a crisis (also very good at just avoiding crisis)

Favorite Movie: For Your Owls Only

Clearance for spying: Third Class Spy Clearance for secrets

Clearance for height: Irrelevant due to flying and all

Fluke Flood

I don't agree with your headline, Newt... Well, I agree I am indeed a famous moose, but not flummoxed!

Do you know what that means, Anonymoose?

Yes...no... mostly. I don't think it sounds good.

It means you are bewildered... stumped by the cause of the flood.

I've never been stumped, just slightly annoyed.

Can we get back to the hit on the bank?

It was the strangest thing. This wall of water just hit the bank and all the vaults got flooded. While we were in such a panic trying to get stuff up on dry land, we think someone scooped up a lot of the money.

They weren't singing and picking up shiny things, were they?

It looks like you saved a lot of data, Chipmunk. We'll have to wade through it and see what we can find out.

That's funny, Owlfred. Wade through it!

You made a joke, Owlfred?

I guess I did! Not feisty but funny. That's a start!

But maybe some of the data can help us find out what happened to Madam HQ.

AGENT MOOSE

58

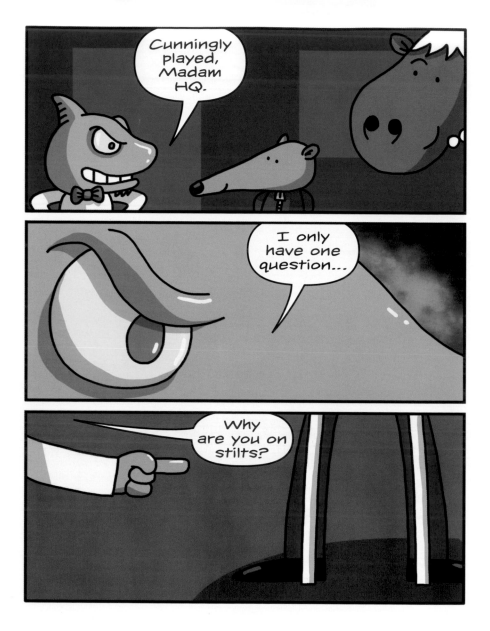

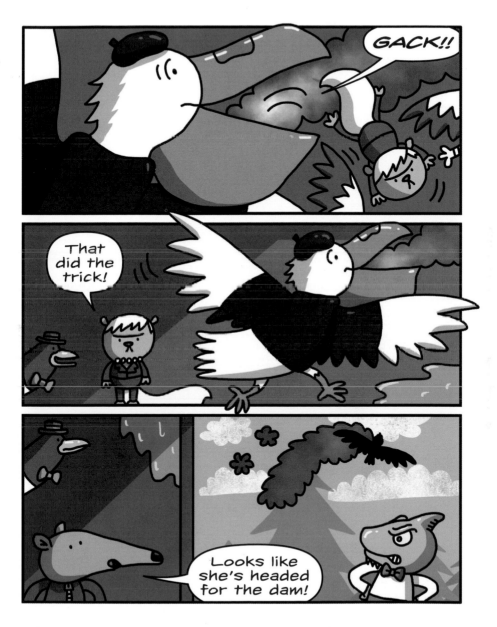

AGENT MOOSE

DAM DISASTER

 AGENT MOOSE

Now that the Big Woods is safe, why don't we drop Camo and Paula at Woodland Prison, and make sure the beavers give the money back and help repair everything as punishment!

I have some ideas on how to rebuild and upgrade Woodland HQ!

And then we can all go for hot cocoa to celebrate.

With marshmallows?

And extra feisty sprinkles!

That sounds like an excellent plan. And I do like a plan!

☆ NEWS OF the WILD ☆

CAMO CAPTURED!!! PAULA IN PRISON!

Master criminals caught by Agent Moose and other members of Woodland HQ today after a confounding kidnap caper. Agent Moose: "I was not confounded either!"

Feisty fashion fad—little red beards are all the rage!	Beavers beaver away at fixing flood damage
	Chipmunk designs new Data Room for rebuilt Woodland HQ!

THANK YOU FOR READING.

The Friends who made

possible are:

Jean Feiwel, Publisher

Liz Szabla, Associate Publisher

Rich Deas, Senior Creative Director

Holly West, Senior Editor

Anna Roberto, Senior Editor

Kat Brzozowski, Senior Editor

Dawn Ryan, Executive Managing Editor

Kim Waymer, Senior Production Manager

Erin Siu, Associate Editor

Emily Settle, Associate Editor

Rachel Diebel, Assistant Editor

Foyinsi Adegbonmire, Associate Editor

Liz Dresner, Associate Art Director

Mandy Veloso, Senior Production Editor